P9-DNG-319

DID

YOU EVER?

by Doris Herold Lund

illustrated by Denman Hampson

For Lisa

Parents' Magazine Press
A Division of Parents' Magazine Enterprises, Inc.
New York

Did you ever
put a mitten on a doorknob
and then . . .

Library of Congress Catalog Card Number 64-19768
Printed in the United States of America

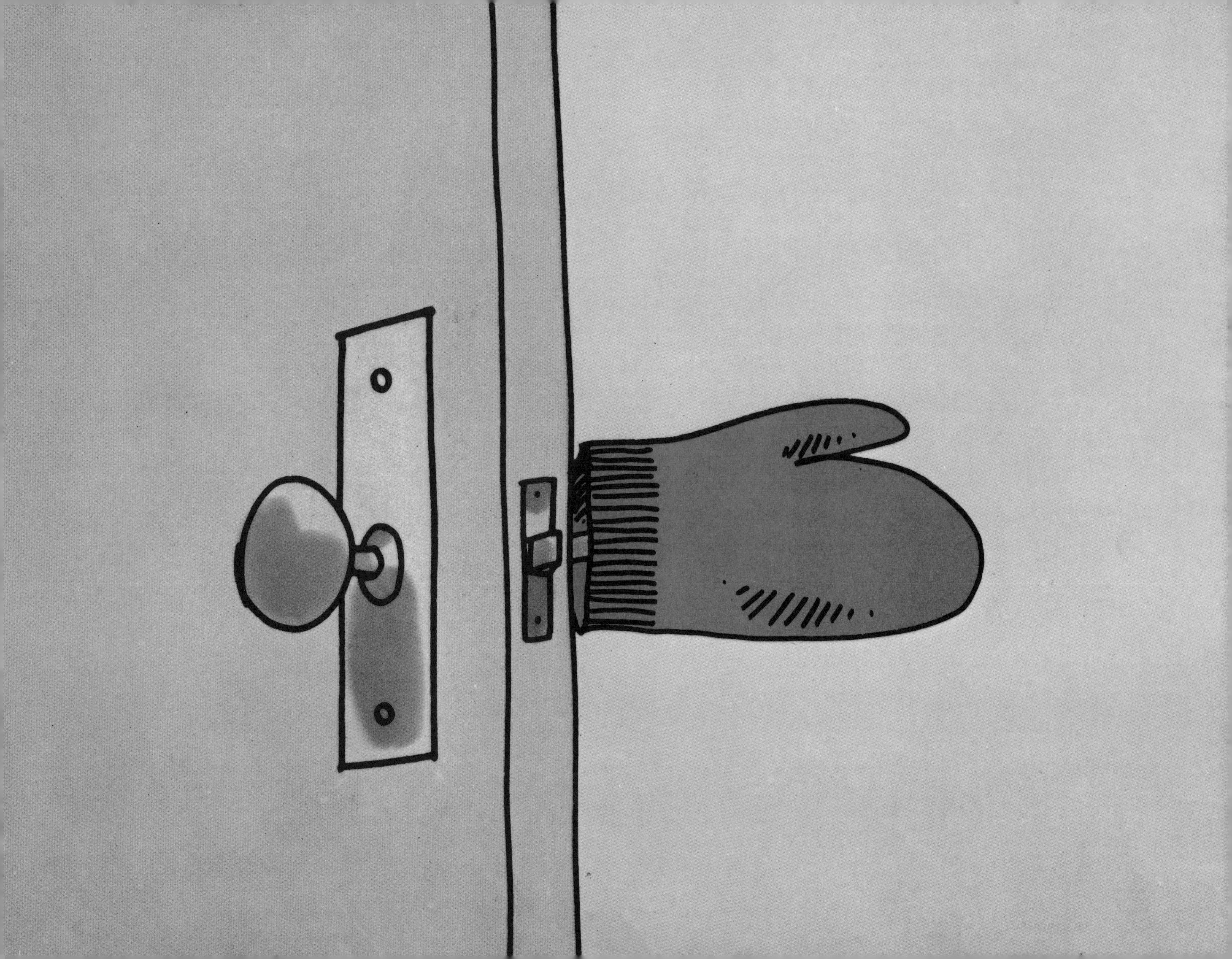

shake hands with a door?

Did you ever
keep losing your hair ribbons
and then . . .

wish you had a hair-ribbon tree
growing in your room?

Did you ever
pull your daddy's hat
down over your head
and then . . .

think it was nighttime?

Did you ever
slide down in the tub
when you were taking a bath
and then . . .

pretend the whole bathroom
was full of sea water
and you were a little fish
swimming around?

Did you ever scrunch down inside
a great big box and then . . .

pop up like a jack-in-the-box
and scare your mother?

Did you ever
draw faces on frosty windows
and then . . .

watch till they melted
and all the faces
began to cry?

Did you ever
warm your pajamas
in front of the fire
and then . . .

get into bed
and feel like a tiger
sleeping in the sun?

Did you ever
lift your face to a gentle rain
and then . . .

when the sun came out,
feel like a daisy opening up to the sky?

Did you ever swing on a rope
from a high branch
and then . . .

think you were a Halloween witch
riding on her broom?

Did you ever
get out some pots and pans
and lids and spoons
and then . . .

invite your friends in
and conduct an orchestra?

Did you ever
take the clothes basket
and crawl under it
and then . . .

stick your head out
and say, "I'm a turtle!"

Did you ever buy
the whole big bunch of balloons
and then . . .

pretend to ride in the sky
high over the trees?

Did you ever lie on your back
a long, long time
and then . . .

get all mixed up
and think the floor was the ceiling
and the ceiling was the floor?

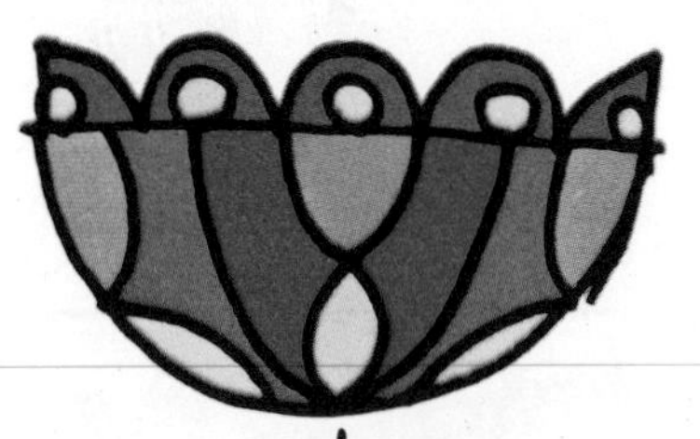

Did you ever play
with all your mother's old jewelry
and then . . .

end up sparkling
like a Christmas tree?

Did you ever go up to the top
of a very tall building
and see the whole world
spread out around you
and then . . .

feel, oh, so happy
to come down and be HOME again!